MOTHER GOOSE

Illustrated by JOSEPH HIRSCH

Wonder Books   NEW YORK

SIMPLE SIMON

Simple Simon met a pieman,
　　Going to the fair;
Says Simple Simon to the pieman,
　　"Let me taste your ware."

Says the pieman to Simple Simon,
　　"Show me first your penny."
Says Simple Simon to the pieman,
　　"Indeed I have not any."

He went to catch a dickey-bird,
　　And thought he could not fail,
Because he'd got a little salt
　　To put upon his tail.

He went to shoot a wild duck,
　　But wild duck flew away;
Says Simon, "I can't hit him,
　　Because he will not stay."

Simple Simon went a-fishing
    For to catch a whale;
All the water he had got
    Was in his mother's pail.

    He went to ride a spotted cow,
      That had a little calf,
    She threw him down upon the ground,
      Which made the people laugh.

Simple Simon went to look
    If plums grew on a thistle;
He pricked his fingers very much,
    Which made poor Simon whistle.

    He went for water in a sieve,
      But soon it all ran through;
    And now poor Simple Simon
      Bids you all adieu.

PETER, PETER, PUMPKIN-EATER

Peter, Peter, pumpkin-eater,
Had a wife and couldn't keep her;
He put her in a pumpkin shell,
And there he kept her very well.

HICKETY, PICKETY

Hickety, pickety, my black hen,
She lays eggs for gentlemen;
Gentlemen come every day
To see what my black hen doth lay.

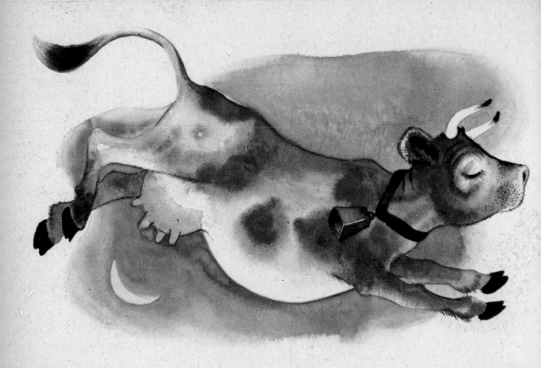

HEY, DIDDLE, DIDDLE

Hey, diddle, diddle, the cat and the fiddle,
The cow jumped over the moon;
The little dog laughed to see such sport,
And the dish ran away with the spoon.

HUMPTY-DUMPTY

Humpty-Dumpty sat on a wall,
Humpty-Dumpty had a great fall;
All the King's horses, and all the King's men,
Couldn't put Humpty-Dumpty together again.

MARY'S LAMB

Mary had a little lamb,
　　Its fleece was white as snow;
And everywhere that Mary went
　　The lamb was sure to go.

It followed her to school one day
　　Which was against the rule;
It made the children laugh and play
　　To see a lamb at school.

HICKORY, DICKORY, DOCK

Hickory, dickory, dock,
The mouse ran up the clock,
The clock struck one,
The mouse ran down;
Hickory, dickory, dock.

BA-A BA-A BLACK SHEEP

Ba-a, ba-a, black sheep, have you any wool?

Yes, sir, yes, sir, three bags full:

One for my master, one for my dame,

But none for the little boy who cries in the lane.

A DILLAR, A DOLLAR

A dillar, a dollar,
A ten o'clock scholar,
What makes you come so soon?
You used to come at ten o'clock,
And now you come at noon.

WEE WILLIE WINKIE

Wee Willie Winkie runs through the town;
Upstairs and downstairs, in his nightgown;
Rapping at the window, crying through the lock,
"Are the children in their beds?
　　　　　For now it's eight o'clock."

OLD MOTHER HUBBARD

Old Mother Hubbard
Went to the cupboard,
   To get her poor Dog a bone;
But when she came there
The cupboard was bare,
   And so the poor Dog has none.

PUSSY CAT,

WHERE HAVE YOU BEEN?

Pussy cat, pussy cat, where have you been?
I've been to London to see the Queen.
Pussy cat, pussy cat, what did you there?
I frightened a little mouse under the chair.

JACK BE NIMBLE

Jack be nimble,
  Jack be quick,
Jack jump over the
  candlestick.

LITTLE TOMMY TUCKER

Little Tommy Tucker
  Sings for his supper.
What shall he eat?
  White bread and butter.

How shall he cut it
  Without any knife?
How shall he marry
  Without any wife?

SING A SONG OF SIXPENCE

Sing a song of sixpence, a pocket full of rye;
 Four and twenty blackbirds baked in a pie;
When the pie was opened, the birds began to sing;
 Wasn't that a dainty dish to set before the king?

The king was in the parlor, counting out his money;
 The queen was in the kitchen,
                    eating bread and honey;
The maid was in the garden, hanging out the clothes;
 Along came a little blackbird,
                    and nipped off her nose.

OLD KING COLE

Old King Cole was a merry old soul
And a merry old soul was he;
He called for his pipe and he called for his glass
And he called for his fiddlers three!

Every fiddler, he had a fine fiddle,
And a very fine fiddle had he.
Oh, there's none so rare as can compare
With King Cole and his fiddlers three!

THIS LITTLE PIG

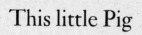

This little Pig 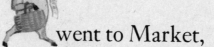 went to Market,

This little Pig stayed at Home,

This little Pig had Roast Beef,

This little Pig had none,

This little Pig cried

wee, wee, wee,

All the way home.

THREE LITTLE KITTENS

Three little kittens lost their mittens,
and they began to cry,
Oh! mother dear, we very much fear
That we have lost our mittens.
Lost your mittens! You naughty kittens!
Then you shall have no pie.
Mee-ow, mee-ow, mee-ow, mee-ow.
No, you shall have no pie.
Mee-ow, mee-ow, mee-ow.

The three little kittens found their mittens,
     and they began to cry,
      Oh! mother dear, see here, see here!
      See, we have found our mittens.
Put on your mittens, you silly kittens, and you
     shall have some pie.

LITTLE BOY BLUE

Little Boy Blue, come, blow your horn;
The sheep's in the meadow, the cow's in the corn.
Where's the boy that looks after the sheep?
He's under the haystack, fast asleep.

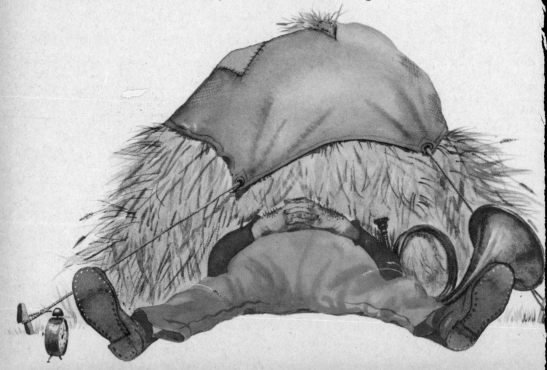